FUN to LEARN
Reading

Dee Reid

Illustrated by Stuart Trotter

Educational Advisory Panel

Bernard Ashley – Head teacher and author

Diana Bentley – Language adviser

Peter Patilla – Lecturer and author

Susie Sainsbury – Nursery teacher

WALKER BOOKS

Notes to Parents

This series of books has been written to help children enjoy books, stories, writing and other related language activities. All children are natural learners and they learn best when they are relaxed, happy and willing participants.

* When using this book do allow your children to decide how long they spend on a chosen activity. Don't worry if they decide not to finish a page. It is far better that they should be allowed to put down a book while they are still enjoying it.

* Do give constant and genuine praise. Children thrive best when they feel they are successful. Do try to recognize the effort they have made. Remember that what appears easy to an adult may require enormous effort on the part of a child.

* All children like sharing a book with an interested adult, so although many activities can be done alone, do try to set aside time to explore this book together.

1 Spot the difference
This is quite a complex picture that needs careful scrutiny for a child to find everything. This activity encourages the careful attention to detail that is so much a part of reading.

2 What am I?
3 Who am I?
While reading these riddles the reader could try to guess the answer before the final clue. Encourage your children to test a listener and see if the listener can get the answer to the riddle before the end. They could also make up their own, perhaps describing members of their family or friends.

4 Treasure hunt
The objects are hidden within the lines and shading of this picture. Children are encouraged to search the picture to find the treasure, at the same time learning to look closely and pay attention to detail.

5 The Trolls' revenge
It is advisable that the reader knows the traditional story of the Three Billy Goats Gruff. Have you ever thought about the story from the Trolls' point of view? Not only will the reader enjoy the humour of this tale but they will be introduced to the more advanced concept of discussing it from different angles. Children need to recognize that there is another point of view in all stories, whether a traditional tale, a factual story or a news item.

6 Sea horses and sharks
This board game can be played by two or more players. It encourages the recognition of words children have already met, without penalizing those who may find this task difficult. It would be a simple matter to place other words on any of the bubbles that children want to read.

7 Fishy business

Following instructions in order to make something is a vital but often difficult task. Show your children the need to check carefully that each instruction is completed before rushing on to the next one. This attention to detail and the methodical approach that is needed will be of value throughout your children's schooling.

8 Shopping list

This Walter Bear story requires the reader to look carefully at the words, for Walter Bear has muddled his shopping and got confused about what he's asking for. This story could be read like a play. Let your children read the part of the friends that Walter Bear meets and you take the part of Walter Bear. As the children become more confident, exchange roles or encourage them to read it producing different voices for the different characters.

9 Junk shop

It is very valuable both in reading and writing for children to recognize when two letters represent a single sound. Finding all the objects that start with these sounds helps to consolidate this skill in a stimulating and challenging way.

10 The story of a sparrow

This information story, which is told without words, encourages children not only to interpret pictures but also to become accustomed to the form of non-fiction. It is possible to start at any point in the cycle. This invites the reader to consider the format of information texts and to make logical connections between facts.

11 What's wrong?

Being able to see when something is illogical and relaying this information to a friend encourages children not to take everything for granted but to question what they see.

12 Tongue-twisters
13 Fishy jokes

Jokes and rhymes are frequently children's first choice of reading matter at this age. They like the challenge of the tongue-twisters and the power they have over their audience when telling or reading a joke.

14 All about me

This page is a simple record for children to keep. Let them practise writing the answer before writing in the book, but at this stage they should be able to fill it in themselves.

Books to share

This book can only provide an introduction to reading skills.
For more extended reading, ask your bookshop or library for some of these titles.

Read-to-Me Books

Julia Donaldson	*The Gruffalo*	Macmillan
Judith Kerr	*The Tiger Who Came to Tea*	Picture Lions
Maurice Sendak	*Where the Wild Things Are*	Red Fox

Read-Alone Books

John Burningham	*Mr Gumpy's Outing*	Red Fox
David McKee	*Not Now, Bernard*	Red Fox
Michael Rosen	*We're Going on a Bear Hunt*	Walker
Elfrida Vipont	*The Elephant and the Bad Baby*	Puffin

1 Spot the differences

Look at the pond.
Can you find two snails?
How are they different?
There are two herons, but are they the same?

Look at the frogs.
Are they the same?
There are lots of differences in this picture.
How many can you find?

2 What am I?

Read these to your friends.
How quickly can they guess the answer?

I have four legs.
I have a head.
I have one foot.
You can sleep in me.
What am I?

I have two wings.
I have no eyes.
I can fly.
You can sit in me.
What am I?

I am fast.
I am long.
I run on rails.
What am I?

I lay eggs.
I can swim.
I can fly.
I say "Quack, quack."
What am I?

I hunt in the dark.
I catch mice and voles.
I say "Twit-a-whoo."
What am I?

3 Who am I?

My porridge was just right.
My chair was not strong.
My bed had someone in it.
Who am I?

I have a long tail.
I have big ears.
I have big teeth.
I like huffing and puffing.
Who am I?

I have to work hard.
I have two sisters.
I went to a ball.
I lost my glass slipper.
Who am I?

I hate noisy footsteps.
I like deep water.
I live under a bridge.
Who am I?

Can you work out all the fairytale characters
round the edge of the page?
Can you make up some other riddles for
your friends?

4 Treasure hunt

The following objects are hidden in the picture:
accordion, barrel, belt, boot, cutlass, dagger, flute, hat,
map, necklace, parrot, pipe, ring, rope.

How many can you find?

5 The Trolls' revenge

Once upon a time there was a family of trolls who lived under a bridge.

They brushed and polished and dusted to keep their house neat.

They were a happy family and they liked to keep their home tidy.

Then one day a family of greedy goats moved into a big field by the bridge.

They ate everything – even Mrs Troll's washing line – but they were still hungry.

One day the smallest goat looked at the grass in a small field on the other side of the bridge.

"There is lots of juicy grass in that small field. I will cross the bridge and eat it all up," he said.

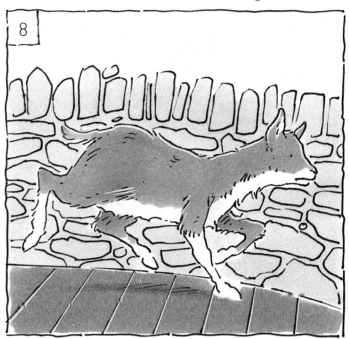

So he ran across the bridge. TRIP TRAP TRIP TRAP.

All that trip-trapping shook the trolls' home. A picture fell and hit Baby Troll on the nose.

The smallest goat didn't care. He munched and munched on the juicy grass.

Mother Goat looked up and saw the smallest goat in the field over the bridge.

"I'll have some too," she said, and she ran across the bridge. TRIP TRAP TRIP TRAP.

The postman asked where he was going.

"To buy a loaf of butter, a packet of beans and a can of bread," said Walter Bear.

Sounds a bit odd, thought the postman.

Next Walter Bear saw a bird in a tree.

The bird asked where he was going.

"To buy a can of butter, a loaf of beans and a packet of bread," said Walter Bear.

Sounds a bit odd, thought the bird.

When he got to the shops Walter Bear asked for a bread of beans, a butter of loaf and a can of packet, please.

All that trip-trapping shook the trolls' home, and the clock fell on Mrs Troll.

Mother Goat didn't care. She munched and munched on the juicy grass.

You greedy goats.

Father Goat looked up. He saw the other goats in the field over the bridge.

"I'll have some too," he said, and he ran across the bridge. TRIP TRAP TRIP TRAP.

All this trip-trapping shook the trolls' home, and a shelf of books fell on Mr Troll's toe.

Father Goat didn't care. He munched and munched on the juicy grass.

Mr Troll did care. He cared about his home and his toe, which hurt.

"You greedy goats will not trip trap over my home again," he said.

3 Put all the fish in a line at one end of the room.
4 Each player stands behind his/her own fish.
5 Give the signal "go" and each player must "flap" his
fish across the room. Remember, hands are banned.
The winner is the first fish across the room.

To make a mobile

You will need: a wire coathanger
at least eight fish
some cotton

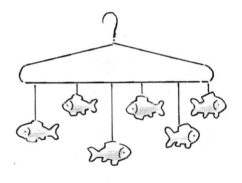

1 Thread the cotton through the centre of each fish's back
and tie carefully.
2 Make some of the pieces of cotton longer than others.
3 Tie the fish onto the coathanger.
4 Move the fish along the coathanger until they balance.
5 Hang your mobile in your room.

8 Shopping list

Walter Bear was going to
the shops.

"I must buy a loaf of bread,
a packet of butter and a can
of beans," he said.

"I mustn't forget anything,"
he said.

He saw the postman on
his bike.

"Are you sure?" asked the
shopkeeper.

Walter Bear thought again.
He went a little red.

"Sorry," he said, "I think I mean
a loaf of bread, a packet of
butter and a can of beans."

Next time I'll write a list,
thought Walter Bear.

9 Junk shop

What can you find in the junk shop beginning with ch, sh and th?

10 The story of a sparrow

Spring

Winter

What does the sparrow use to build its nest?
How many eggs can you see?
What do the baby sparrows eat?

Summer

Autumn

Where do the sparrows find their food in the winter?
Can you tell the story of the sparrow?

11 What's wrong?

There are 20 funny things to be found in this seaside picture.

Can you spot them?

12　Tongue-twisters

Whether the weather be hot,
Or whether the weather be cold,
We'll weather the weather
Whatever the weather
Whether we like it or not.

She sells seashells
On the seashore
The shells that she sells
Are seashells, I'm sure.

Peter Piper picked a peck of pickled pepper.
If Peter Piper picked a peck of pickled pepper
Where's the peck of pickled
pepper Peter Piper picked?

13   Fishy jokes

Why are goldfish red?
Because the water makes them rusty.

What's the difference between a fish and a piano?
You can't tuna fish.

Who ate his dinner two by two?
Noah Shark.

Where do you go to weigh a whale?
To the whale weigh station.

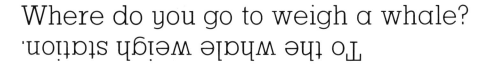

What's yellow and dangerous?
Shark-infested custard.

What do police fish ride in?
A squid car.

What goes through the water at 100 mph?
A motor pike.

14   All about me

My name is _____

I am _____ cm tall. _____

I go to _____ school.

I weigh _____ kilograms.

My friends are _____

I have lost _____ teeth.

Draw a picture or stick a
photograph of yourself here.

I would like a _____ as a pet.

When I grow up I would like to be a _____

First published 1990 by Walker Books Ltd
87 Vauxhall Walk, London SE11 5HJ

This edition published 2003

10 9 8 7 6 5 4 3 2 1

Text © 1990 Dee Reid
Illustrations © 1990 Stuart Trotter

The right of Dee Reid and Stuart Trotter to be identified as
author and illustrator respectively of this work has been
asserted by them in accordance with the Copyright, Designs
and Patents Act 1988

This book has been typeset in Rockwell Light Educational

Printed in Italy

All rights reserved.

British Library Cataloguing in Publication Data:
a catalogue record for this book is available from the British
Library

ISBN 1-84428-798-X

www.walkerbooks.co.uk